DVD SERIES

THE FOUNDATIONS

Psalm 11:3

1:1

Answers
IN GENESIS™

The *Foundations* Participant Workbook

Copyright © 2011 Answers in Genesis–USA

Reprinted February 2020

All rights reserved. No part of this publication may be reproduced in any manner whatsoever without written permission from the publisher.

Scripture taken from the New King James Version®. Copyright © 1982 by Thomas Nelson. Used by permission. All rights reserved.

For more information write:
Answers in Genesis, PO Box 510, Hebron, KY 41048

ISBN: 978-1-60092-434-7

Compiled by Gary Vaterlaus
Edited by Anneliese Rumminger
Interior layout by Diane King
Packaging and cover design by Brandie Lucas

Printed in China

Table of Contents

Objectives

It is our prayer that after you have finished these lessons you will be able to . . .

- Identify how the foundations have been destroyed in our Western culture.
- Identify how the church has compromised God's Word.

Introduction

Years ago, our society was based on Christian absolutes. People knew what was right and what was wrong. Behaviors such as sexual deviancy, easy divorce, public lawlessness, abortion on demand, pornography, and public nudity were considered to be wrong. Varying punishments for offenders were meted out by society. Value judgments were basically built on biblical principles (for example, the Ten Commandments). Most people accepted or respected a belief in God.

In recent decades, more and more people have rejected the God of the Bible. As belief in God has been abandoned, people have questioned the basis of the society in which they live. For instance, if there is no God, then why should they obey the Ten Commandments? Why should anyone say that homosexuality is wrong? Why should women be barred from having abortions whenever they desire? Once people eliminated God from their consciences, they set about to change any laws based on Christian absolutes that held God as Creator (and thus owner) of everything.

Christian absolutes—those truths and standards of Scripture which cannot be altered—are becoming less and less tolerated in society. Eventually this must result in the marginalizing (if not outlawing) of Christianity. When Christian absolutes were the basis of society, immoral activities such as homosexual or lesbian lifestyles and pornography were outlawed. There has been a fundamental shift. Our society is now based on a relative morality: that is, a person can do what he likes and is answerable to no one but himself as long as the majority of people can be persuaded that their interests are not being threatened. This results in society being told that no one can say anything against those who choose to be sexual deviants, go naked publicly, or do whatever they want (within the limits of the law, which is also changing to become more "tolerant" of people's deviant behavior).

God's absolutes dictate that there are rules by which we must abide. Christianity cannot coexist in a world community with relative morality as its basis. One or the other will yield. There are two worldviews with two totally different belief systems clashing in our society. The real war being waged is a great spiritual war. Sadly, today many Christians fail to win the war because they fail to recognize the nature of the battle.

It is my contention that this spiritual conflict is rooted in the issue of origins (creation/evolution). Although the thought may sound strange or new to you, biblically and logically this issue is central in the battle for men's souls.

(From *The Lie: Evolution* by Ken Ham, chapter 1)

Video Viewing Guide

The Collapse of the Western World

> 1 Chronicles 12:32 – The sons of Issachar had "understanding of the times." Do we know what is happening in our nation and in our Western world?

> Psalm 11:3 – "If the foundations are destroyed, what can the righteous do?" The foundation of the authority of the Word of God has come under attack throughout our Western world.

> 1 Peter 3:15 – "Always be ready to give a defense," or an answer. Apologia (Greek) – apologetics – to give a logical, reasoned defense of the faith. Most Christians don't know how to answer the skeptical questions of our age. We need to be teaching apologetics.

> Mark 16:15 – "Go into all the world and preach the gospel to every creature." We live in an increasingly skeptical culture in which many people don't even listen to the gospel because they don't believe the book from which it comes. We need to understand how we're going to approach such people.

> What's happening in England is happening in America. Where England is today, America will be tomorrow.

> In England, two thirds of teenagers don't believe in God. If nearly two thirds of teenagers don't believe in God, where are the culture and church going to be in the next couple of generations?

> The atheists are really on the march . . . in England and increasingly in America.

> In Australia, the number of churchgoers is at nine percent and dwindling.

> In Canada, weekly church attendance dropped to just over 30% in 1975, and to around 20% in 2000.

> In Western Europe, church attendance is less than 10% in most countries.

> What about in America? We are the greatest Christianized nation in the world. We have more Christian resources right now than any country in the world. But as a culture is American becoming more Christian every year, or less Christian?

> Why is the church not touching the culture? Because the culture has actually invaded the church.

Collapse of the American Culture

> "The Decline and Fall of Christian America" – *Newsweek*, 2009.

> President Obama in *The Audacity of Hope* – "Whatever we once were, we are no longer just a Christian nation."

> If our ideals and values don't come from an absolute authority— God, the Bible—then who decides? It's whoever is in power decides what those ideals and values are—it all becomes relative on who can impose those on a culture.

> "My expectation is that when you look back on these years . . . you will see a time in which we as a nation finally recognize relationships between two men or two women as just as real and admirable as relationships between a man and a woman." – President Obama, 2009.

> "Increasingly, supernatural faith belongs to the third world. The first world is entering the long-predicted Secular Age, when science and knowledge dominate." – Free Inquiry, February 2010.

> Atheists are very aggressive in getting their message out—on billboards, on buses, etc.

> "So forget Jesus, the stars died so that you could be here today." – Lawrence Kraus, 2009.

Collapse of the American Church

> Barna Research (2002, 2006) – Two thirds of young people are walking away from church by college age. If that keeps happening in our churches, where's the church in America going to be?

> It only takes one generation to lose an entire culture.

> Already Gone Research (2009) – Hypocrisy is one of the main reasons young people are leaving the church—going to church and being told, "We believe the Bible, trust in Jesus," and then being told, "We don't necessarily believe this part of the Bible."

We've always been trying to prepare our kids for college . . . but it turns out that only 11 percent of those who have left the Church did so during the college years. Almost 90 percent of them were lost in middle school and high school. By the time they got to college they were already gone! About 40 percent are leaving the Church during elementary and middle school years! Most people assumed that elementary and middle school is a fairly neutral environment where children toe the line and follow in the footsteps of their parents' spirituality. Not so. I believe that over half of these kids were lost before we got them into high school! Whatever diseases are fueling the epidemic of losing our young people, they are infecting our students much, much earlier than most assumed. (Ken Ham & Britt Beemer, *Already Gone*, chapter 1)

> The same basic questions are asked all the time:

- How do you know the Bible is true?
- Where did the Bible come from?
- Where did God come from?
- Who made God?
- How do you know that there's a God?
- Why those 66 books?
- Carbon-14 disproves the Bible.
- What about dinosaurs—how do you explain that if the Bible's true?
- We know there wasn't a global flood. There's not enough water to cover the earth for a global flood.
- Noah couldn't fit all the animals on the Ark.

> The secularists are capturing the hearts and minds of generations of our kids and teaching them why the Bible, from their perspective, can't be trusted and is not true.

Group Discussion Questions

1. Ken says that atheists are "on the march." Have you seen atheists becoming more active and aggressive in our culture?

2. What have you noticed in the last 10 to 20 years that illustrates Ken's assertion that America is becoming increasingly secular?

3. Why do you think America is becoming less Christian every year?

4. Do you agree with Ken's assessment of today's youth and the reasons they are leaving church?

5. Do you know any youth who have left the church? What do you think were their reasons?

6. How important is it that we be teaching our children to answer the skeptical questions of the age?

For Personal Reflection

1. Are you equipped to answer the questions that Ken listed (see p. 10)? Why or why not? How might you get equipped?

2. Have you and your family unwittingly adopted the secular culture or been brainwashed by evolutionary thinking? In what ways? What can you do about it?

For Next Week

Please read and meditate on the following verses in preparation for next week's lesson:

- Genesis 1:1–31
- Exodus 20:8–11
- 2 Peter 1:19–21
- 2 Timothy 3:14–17

For Further Study

- Searching for the "Magic Bullet" – www.answersingenesis.org/creation/v25/i2/bullet.asp
- Creation: Where's the Proof? – www.answersingenesis.org/creation/v22/i1/creation.asp
- Get Answers – www.answersingenesis.org/get-answers

Resources

- *The Lie: Evolution* by Ken Ham, Master Books
- *The New Answers Books*, volumes 1–3, edited by Ken Ham, Master Books
- *Already Gone* by Ken Ham & Britt Beemer, Master Books

Lesson 2: Relevance of Genesis – Part 2

Objectives

It is our prayer that after you have finished these lessons you will be able to . . .

- Understand how Genesis 1–11 is foundational to the rest of the Bible and the gospel message.
- Recognize the key to changing the culture.

Introduction

In the past, Christian symbols in public places, the Bible and prayer in public schools, etc., were reminders to the coming generations of the Christian heritage of this nation. They were also a witness to other nations concerning the true God and the truth of His Word. America has been a great Christian witness in the past, but this has changed markedly. America has become a secularized country; moral relativism has permeated the culture.

This nation has changed foundation: from God's Word to man's word. This transformation has occurred in the government, the courts, the education system, and also to a large degree in the church. Because many churches and Bible colleges/seminaries have compromised God's Word with the pagan religion of the age (millions of years/evolution) that tries to explain life without God, the church has helped undermine biblical authority in America. In so doing, Christians have actually paved the way for the nation's change, helping (unwittingly in most cases) to build a worldview-foundation that is becoming more man-centered and less Bible-centered.

Also, many in the church and culture have been duped into thinking that the so-called "separation of church and state" issue (a perversion of what the First Amendment actually states concerning freedom of religion) means that the Bible and Christian symbols should be eliminated from the public sector, and thus bring in a neutral situation. But there is no such position as neutrality. Think about it. One is either for Christ or against Him! What has happened is that the religion of naturalism (atheism) has been imposed on the public education system (and on the culture as a whole).

The only way for the Christian reminders that have been removed to be restored is for Christians and the culture to return to the authoritative Word of God as the foundation for all thinking. After all, "Blessed is the nation whose God is the LORD" (Psalm 33:12).

(From "The State of the Nation" by Ken Ham, www.answersingenesis.org/articles/2010/03/08/state-of-the-nation)

Video Viewing Guide

The Religion of Atheism

> The secularists understand, "If we can get the kids, we'll get the culture."

> Due to the so-called "separation of church and state" issue, there's this idea that if you mention God, that's religious; if you don't, that's not religious. Actually, if you mention God, that's religious; if you don't mention God, that's religious. There is no neutral position. Jesus said you are either for him or against him; you either gather or scatter.

> Our culture has removed the foundation of the authority of the Word of God.

> The church has adopted the pagan religion of the age (evolution and millions of years) into our culture, and it's contaminated the Word of God, and we wonder why we're losing our culture.

The Importance of Genesis 1–11

› When we say that you can add millions of years and evolution into the Bible, and we reinterpret what Genesis clearly teaches, we do two things:

1. We undermine the history that is foundational to all doctrine.

2. We undermine the very Word of God itself.

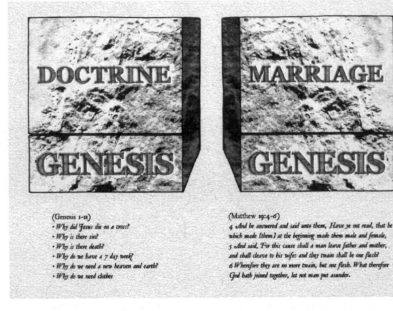

(Genesis 1–11)
- Why did Jesus die on a cross?
- Why is there sin?
- Why is there death?
- Why do we have a 7 day week?
- Why do we need a new heaven and earth?
- Why do we need clothes?

(Matthew 19:4-6)
4 And he answered and said unto them, Have ye not read, that he which made [them] at the beginning made them male and female,
5 And said, For this cause shall a man leave father and mother, and shall cleave to his wife: and they twain shall be one flesh?
6 Wherefore they are no more twain, but one flesh. What therefore God hath joined together, let not man put asunder.

› Do you realize ultimately every single biblical doctrine of theology, directly or indirectly, is founded in Genesis 1–11?

- Why did Jesus die on the Cross?

- Why is there sin in the world?

- Why is there death?

- Why do we have a seven-day week?

- Why do we need a new heavens and a new earth?

- Why do we wear clothes?

If you destroy the foundations of anything, the structure will collapse. If you want to destroy any building, you are guaranteed early success if you destroy the foundations.

Likewise, if one wants to destroy Christianity, then destroy the foundations established in the Book of Genesis. Is it any wonder that Satan is attacking Genesis more than any other book?

The biblical doctrine of origins, as contained in the Book of Genesis, is foundational to all other doctrines of Scripture. Refute or undermine in any way the biblical doctrine of origins, and the rest of the Bible is compromised. Every single biblical doctrine of theology, directly or indirectly, ultimately has its basis in the Book of Genesis. (Ken Ham, *The Lie: Evolution*, Chapter 4)

> Some parents and pastors say, "It doesn't matter what you believe about Genesis. What's most important is that you trust in Jesus." But . . .

- How do we know Jesus Christ bodily rose from the dead?
- How do we know about the virgin birth?
- How do we know a fish swallowed a man?
- How do we know Jesus walked on water?
- How do we know the Israelites crossed the Red Sea on dry land?
- How do we know Jesus multiplied loaves and fishes and fed thousands of people?
- How do we know the walls of Jericho fell down?

> Church leaders in the late 1700s, early 1800s, in England unlocked the door to compromise: "You don't have to take God's Word as written; you can use man's ideas outside the Bible, reinterpret the Bible."

> When there's compromise or sin in one generation, is it usually to a greater or lesser extent in the next? Greater.

› You don't need to believe in a literal Genesis and a young earth to be saved.

› Salvation is not conditioned upon the age of the earth or the days of creation, but it's conditioned upon faith in Christ. But where does the message of Jesus come from? The Word of God. And if you can't trust the Word of God over here, why should you be able to trust it over here.

› If the first four C's are not true—Creation, Corruption, Catastrophe, Confusion (the history in Genesis 1–11)— then neither is the rest—Christ, Cross, Consummation.

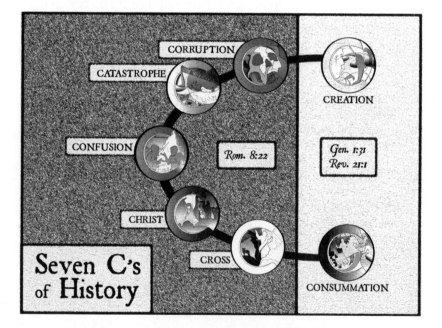

> Instead of teaching children Bible "stories," we should be teaching them real history. We need to be preparing generations today to be able to stand on the authority of the Word of God and to give answers. For example:

- Noah's Ark was a real ship—not an overloaded bathtub about ready to tip over, like we show in so many children's Bibles and story books.

- How did Noah fit all the animals on the Ark? He only needed to bring *kinds* on the Ark, not all the *species*.

- Geology supports the idea of a global Flood: we find billions of dead things buried in rock layers laid down by water all over the earth.

Incompatibility of Millions of Years and the Bible

> Men and animals were originally plant eaters (Genesis 1:29–30). It wasn't until after the Flood that man was given permission to eat everything (Genesis 9:3). There was no death before sin. All was "very good" (Genesis 1:31).

(Genesis 3:6)

6 And when the woman saw that the tree was good for food, and that it was pleasant to the eyes, and a tree to be desired to make one wise, she took of the fruit thereof, and did eat, and gave also unto her husband with her; and he did eat.

(Genesis 2:16-17)

16 And the Lord God commanded the man, saying, Of every tree of the garden thou mayest freely eat 17 But of the tree of the knowledge of good and evil, thou shalt not eat of it: for in the day that thou eatest thereof thou shalt surely die.

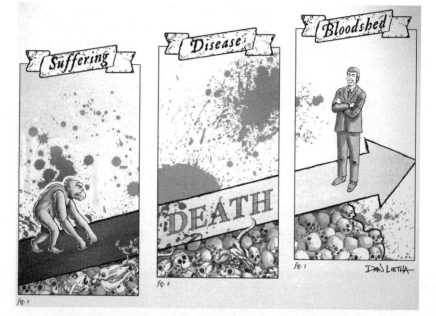

fig. 1   *fig. 2*   *fig. 3*   DAN LIETHA

> If you add millions of years to the Bible, if the fossil record was laid down millions of years before man, then you have death, disease, cancer, and animals eating each other before the Fall, then you undermine the authority of the Word of God.

> As we teach our children to stand on the authority of Scripture and what God said He did, we also need to be showing them how scientific evidences confirm what the Bible teaches. For example,

- Mount St. Helens—sedimentary layers were formed in hours; canyons were formed in days or weeks.
- Grand Canyon—rock layers were bent when they were still soft; this happened at the end of the Flood.

> America has changed religion. It's changed foundation from God's Word to man's word. The church has changed foundation. When we adopt man's word into the Bible and add evolution, millions of years into the Bible, our starting point is no longer God's Word, our starting point is man's world.

› How is much of the church responding to how the culture is going? Instead of understanding the foundational reasons to what's happening, they water down the teaching of the Word and increase entertainment programs.

The Solution

› The castle diagram illustrates that there are only two religions in the world. You either start with God's Word or man's word. You either believe God's Word or decide truth for yourself.

› The moral problems in our culture are not the problems; they are the symptoms of what's happening foundationally.

› The Bible does not say to go into all the world and change the culture; it says to go into all the world and preach the gospel and make disciples.

> We have got to be out there capturing, for the Lord, hearts and minds, raising up generations who will stand on the authority of the Word of God, who know how to defend their faith, know how to give answers to the skeptical questions of this age, because it's those people who will be salt and light and change the culture.

> The solution is that we need to be restoring the authority of the Word of God starting in our homes and churches.

Group Discussion Questions

1. When Bible reading and prayer were removed from the government schools, was religion removed? Why or why not?

2. Ken stated that 90% of church kids go to government schools. How can the church engage these children to be sure they don't adopt the pagan religion of our age?

3. What are some important Bible teachings that are founded, directly or indirectly, in Genesis 1–11?

4. Where do we get information about the gospel?

5. Are miracles scientific? How does this impact our understanding and belief in the Genesis account of creation?

6. If one's belief about the age of the earth and the days of creation is not a salvation issue, then does it matter what one believes about creation and the age of the earth? Explain.

7. How does starting from a biblical perspective help us understand that the hot social issues of today are really symptoms and not problems? What is the underlying problem behind all of these issues?

8. Is it enough to just call for a return to family values or conservative values? Why or why not?

9. How does millions of years of death, disease, and bloodshed before sin undermine the gospel?

For Personal Reflection

1. Do you feel equipped to answer questions about creation, the Flood, and Genesis 1–11? Why or why not?

2. Ken said that we need to restore the authority of the Word of God starting in our homes and churches. Have you equipped your children to defend their faith and the Bible in today's skeptical world? If not, what can you start doing now?

For Next Week

Please read and meditate on the following verses in preparation for next week's lesson:

- Romans 1:16–25
- Romans 10:14–16
- Psalm 19:1–14

For Further Study

- Two Histories of Death – www.answersingenesis.org/creation/v24/i1/history.asp
- The Evolutionizing of a Culture – www.answersingenesis.org/articles/nab2/the-evolutionizing-of-a-culture
- Get Answers – www.answersingenesis.org/get-answers

Resources

- *The Lie: Evolution* by Ken Ham, Master Books
- *The New Answers Books*, volumes 1–3, edited by Ken Ham, Master Books
- *Already Gone* by Ken Ham & Britt Beemer, Master Books

Lesson 3: Always Ready, Apologia – Part 1

Objectives

It is our prayer that after you have finished these lessons you will be able to . . .

- Recognize that the Bible is a record of the past from an Eyewitness who does not lie and knows everything.
- Understand that the Bible must be our starting point when defending the faith.

Introduction

Sadly, most Christians have been educated in a secular education system that indoctrinates them to believe that humans start with evidence to determine beliefs about the past. That is simply not true! Everyone starts with certain beliefs that determine how the evidence is interpreted, even though most people have not consciously thought about what their starting beliefs are.

Because Christians have been indoctrinated in a secular system, they don't know how to approach answering questions about dinosaurs, the age of the earth, and so on. By and large, they don't realize that the secularists who taught them start with presuppositions that disallow the Bible's revelation.

These Christians, who may be real born-again Christians, are secularized in their thinking. So, they ask questions like "How do you fit dinosaurs into the Bible?" Well, you really don't! When we understand the right way to think as a Christian, we know that we should start with the Bible (the revelation from our infinite Creator) and build our thinking (worldview) upon that. Then we have the right way to look at the evidence of the present.

The Bible's accounts of the creation of land animals, their diet before the Fall, the Flood of Noah's day, and so on give us the right foundation to approach the topic of dinosaurs.

Now don't misunderstand me here. The Bible is not a scientific textbook, per se. The word *science* basically means "knowledge." Observational science, based on repeatable tests, is what builds technology. However, historical science (knowledge concerning the past to explain the present) is based on beliefs concerning history. The Bible is primarily a history book—an account of historical science, if you like—to enable us to think correctly concerning the origin of the universe, the meaning of life, the dilemma of sin, and the solution in Jesus Christ.

(From "Not Ashamed of a Biblical Starting Point" by Ken Ham, *Answers*, Jan–Mar, 2010)

Video Viewing Guide

> Romans 1:20 – God is known from His creation.

> Romans 10:17 – Faith comes by hearing and hearing by the Word of God.

> > How can we establish beyond doubt the details of an event that supposedly happened in the past? One way is to find witnesses who were there, or look for records written by witnesses. Therefore, the only way we can ever know for sure exactly what happened in the geological past is if there was someone who was there at the time (a witness) who could tell us whether geological processes have always been the same or whether at some time geological processes have been different. The Bible claims to be the record of One (God) who not only knows everything, but who has always been there because He is outside of time. In fact, He created time. The Bible claims that God moved men through His Spirit to write down His words, and that they are not just the words of men but the Word of God (1 Thess. 2:13, 2 Pet. 1:20–21). The Book of Genesis claims to be the records from God telling us of the events of creation and of other events in this world's early history which have great bearing upon our present circumstances. Thus, the present is not the key to the past. Rather, revelation is the key to the past. (Ken Ham, **The Lie: Evolution**, Chapter 10)

Two Very Different Views of History

> Ultimately there are only two ways of understanding reality. You either start with God's Word—the Word of One who knows everything, who has all information, who gives us the information we need—or somehow man has to figure it out.

> Secularists, who don't believe in God's Word, are here in the present, and they're trying to work from the present into the past to understand what happened in the past.

> The Christian has a revelation from someone who says, "Here's what happened in the past." So we work from what happened in the past to the present.

> Here's the view of the government education system, which has thrown God out:

  • There was a big bang 15 billion years ago.

  • 10 billion years ago the stars formed.

  • 5 billion years ago the sun formed.

  • 4.5 billion years ago a molten earth formed.

  • 3.8 billion years ago water cooled on the earth.

  • Eventually life formed.

> Charles Darwin said, given enough time, the small changes we see will add up to big changes to change one kind of animal into another. Supposedly, over millions of years as life evolved; death, bloodshed, disease, suffering is all a part of this process. Eventually, ape-like creatures turned into people. Supposedly the record of the evolutionary history of life is left in the fossil record.

> The Bible talks about the origin of time, the origin of space, the origin of the earth, the origin of water, the origin of dry land, the origin of plants, the origin of the sun, the origin of the moon, the origin of the stars, the origin of flying creatures, the origin of sea creatures, the origin of land creatures, the origin of man, the origin of woman, the origin of marriage, the origin of sin, the origin of death, the origin of nations, the origin of languages, the origin of clothing.

> Do you know any other book that does that?

> We can summarize that history from Genesis to Revelation, the first book to the last book, as the Seven C's of History:

1. Creation –

2. Corruption –

3. Catastrophe –

4. Confusion –

5. Christ –

6. Cross –

7. Consummation –

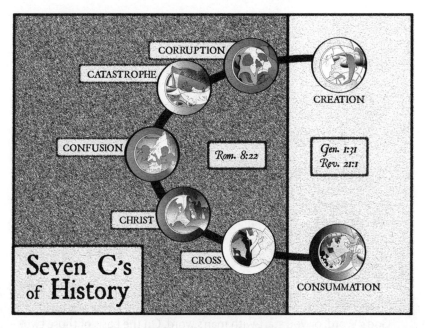

Seven C's of History

CORRUPTION
CATASTROPHE
CONFUSION
CHRIST
CROSS
CREATION
CONSUMMATION
Rom. 8:22
Gen. 1:31
Rev. 21:1

> These are two totally different accounts of history:

Evolution/Millions of Years	Biblical Creation
Big bang	No big bang
Billions of years	Thousands of years
Death has always been here	Death is an intrusion—it's an enemy
Man and woman from ape-like creatures	Man from dust; woman from his side
No global flood	Global flood
No purpose and meaning	Purpose and meaning

> We all have the same facts. What's different is how we interpret that evidence in the context of history.

> There are ultimately only two starting points. You either start with God's Word, or you start with man's word. On the basis of those two starting points, we build a worldview.

> We interpret the evidence from our starting point—the Bible.

- DNA – an information system that can only come from an intelligence

- Kinds – change within kinds; not one kind changing into another

- The human race – there's only one race

> We must recognize the difference between observational/operational science and historical science.

> When it comes to origins, we want to have knowledge. But we need all knowledge to make sure we got it right, which means we need Someone who is omniscient.

> We have a book that claims to be a revelation from God. And, in fact, when you look at that history, it makes sense of the world.

> If it's a random universe, why do we have the laws of nature? If it's a random universe, why do we have the laws of logic?

> Non-Christians must borrow from biblical presuppositions when they do research or argue against God and the Bible

Group Discussion Questions

1. What is the difference between observational science and historical science? How does this affect the origins debate?

2. Summarize the Seven C's of History.

3. Can an atheist account for the laws of nature or the laws of logic? Explain.

4. What does Ken mean when he says that non-Christians have to borrow from biblical presuppositions to even do their research?

For Personal Reflection

1. Is your starting point always the Word of God? Do you look at everything through the lens of Scripture? In which areas do you fall short?

2. Can you explain to someone how what we know about DNA and genetics actually confirm the biblical record of creation, the Fall, and the Tower of Babel? [If not, learn how at AnswersinGenesis.org.]

For Next Week

Please read and meditate on the following verses in preparation for next week's lesson:

- John 16:7–11
- Ephesians 1–2
- 2 Timothy 2:20–26

For Further Study

- Atheism: An Irrational Worldview – www.answersingenesis.org/articles/aid/v2/n1/atheism-irrational
- God and Natural Law – www.answersingenesis.org/articles/am/v1/n2/god-natural-law
- Get Answers – www.answersingenesis.org/get-answers

Resources

- *Ultimate Apologetics* DVD series, featuring Jason Lisle, Answers in Genesis
- *Apologetics Classroom* DVD Series, featuring Mike Riddle, Creation Training Initiative
- *Always Ready*, Greg Bahnsen, Covenant Media Press

Lesson 4: Always Ready, Apologia – Part 2

Objectives

It is our prayer that after you have finished these lessons you will be able to . . .

- Recognize that real science, properly interpreted, confirms the history in the Bible.
- Explain the weaknesses of the Intelligent Design Movement.

Introduction

I think we are sometimes very guilty of giving the wrong idea to the non-Christian when we look at nature and say, "Can't you see there's a God? Look how beautiful this world is? Can't you see there's a God?" And they're looking out there and you know what they are seeing? They're seeing people dying; they're seeing tragedies; they're seeing suffering; they're seeing death; they're seeing disease—and they don't see a beautiful world.

I even think we are sometimes giving the wrong message to our kids through most of our Sunday school literature. When we want to talk to kids about God being "the great Designer" or "the great Creator," we often turn to nature as an example of His creative "beauty." Look at the pictures you see in the Sunday school books and in Christian school textbooks, aren't they "beautiful"? Sure, look how God beautifully designed this little fox to rip the insides out of the bunny! See the dinosaur bones? Yeah, his body was crushed under the weight of tons of sediment. Look how that mosquito sucks the blood out of that little fawn!

We point at nature and life and teach our kids to sing "All things bright and beautiful! The Lord God made them all!" In reality, maybe we should be teaching them to sing "All things maimed and mangled! The Lord God cursed them all!"

In nature, we do see a remnant of beauty, a shattered reflection of the original perfection of Eden. But it's all in the context of death and destruction . . . all of it. Take the Grand Canyon, for example. If you took a non-Christian to this magnificent place—and it is magnificent, by the way; the views are indescribable, particularly at sunrise and sunset—and the two of you were sitting on the edge of the mile-deep canyon, and you say to your friend, "Can't you see there is a God of love in the beauty of what He has created?" Would that be an accurate lead in to a spiritual conversation? Is nature really an illustration of His love?

Certainly there is a beauty there, but it's not an expression of love. The Grand Canyon is residue from a cataclysmic act of God's judgment, a violent worldwide Flood that tore into the earth and entombed billions of living organisms. That's the real bigger picture, and to communicate something else to a non-believer isn't communicating biblical Christianity.

(From *How Could a Loving God?* by Ken Ham, chapter 1)

Video Viewing Guide

> We can actually use observational science to confirm which starting point does make sense of the world.

- DNA actually confirms that there are distinct kinds, and there's no mechanism to change one kind into another.

- When you look at fossils and rock layers all over the earth, actually it confirms catastrophism—that to lay down the rock layers, to form the canyons, to form the fossils is consistent with catastrophic processes covering something suddenly, not slow processes over millions of years.

- And when you look at the human race, observational science confirms one race—just what you'd expect on the basis of Scripture.

> God's Word is the right starting point.

If the Bible is really what it claims to be, a revelation from an omnipotent Creator, then the history that is revealed to us will make sense of the evidence of the present, and observational (empirical) science should confirm this history—and it does!

- The design in living things confirms an incredible intelligence behind the universe.

- The six-day Creation Week (and one day of rest) makes sense of the seven-day week we all adhere to.

- The giving of clothes after Adam and Eve sinned makes sense of why we wear clothes.

- Adam's original sin and its consequence explain why we all die.

- The Flood of Noah's day makes sense of most of the fossil record over the earth.

- The Tower of Babel makes sense of the different languages and nations, and yet genetics confirms we are all one race—consistent with humans being descendants of Adam and Eve. (Ken Ham, "Not Ashamed of a Biblical Starting Point," *Answers*, February 24, 2010.)

Leave the Bible Out of It?

> If you don't use the Bible—if you give up your starting point (and there are only two starting points), then you're left with only one starting point: man's word. It's not a neutral position.

> Romans 1:20 is the Intelligent Design verse of the Bible. It's obvious from creation that there's a God.

> Looking at creation through the Word of God, we understand that sin, death, and suffering came as a result of the Fall. It is our fault, not God's fault.

> If you look at the creation and say there's an intelligence responsible for this, is that intelligence an ogre? Is that intelligence responsible for all the suffering and death we see in the world?

> Romans 10:17 – So then faith comes by hearing, and hearing by the word of God.

> If you're not using intelligent design arguments in the context of the Word of God, then you could drive people in the direction of a false god.

Sin and the Curse

(Genesis 3:6)

6 And when the woman saw that the tree was good for food, and that it was pleasant to the eyes, and a tree to be desired to make one wise, she took of the fruit thereof, and did eat, and gave also unto her husband with her; and he did eat.

DEATH

fig. 1

fig. 2

fig. 3

SIN

(Genesis 2:16-17)

16 And the Lord God commanded the man, saying, Of every tree of the garden thou mayest freely eat 17 But of the tree of the knowledge of good and evil, thou shalt not eat of it: for in the day that thou eatest thereof thou shalt surely die.

> We must not give those intelligent design arguments devoid of the context of Scripture, the Word of God. Those two go together. If you're not using God's Word, there is only one other starting point. That is man's word, and that's not a neutral position.

No Neutral Position

> The Bible says the knowledge of God is written on our hearts. It's crying out, "There's a God!" And so to overcome that, people suppress the truth in unrighteousness, and they actively fight against it. They're suppressing the truth because they don't want to acknowledge that they're a sinner in submission to a Creator.

> Atheists and secular science do not take a neutral position; they leave God out of it.

> It's God's Word that is living and powerful and sharper than any two-edged sword. It's God's Word that goes forth from His mouth and shall not return unto Him void.

> We need to be on the offensive and not throw our sword down. We can show them how our starting point—the Bible—explains the world.

> You see, we all have that starting point. Either God's Word or man's word. When Christians accommodate millions of years and evolution into the Bible, as soon as you introduce fallible man into God's infallible Word, your starting point is no longer God's Word.

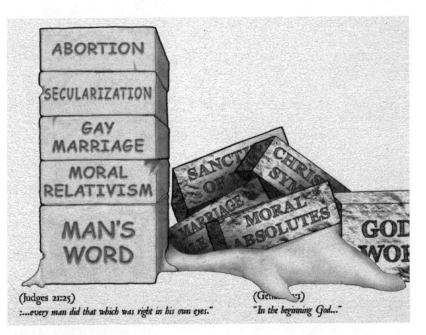

(Judges 21:25)
:...*every man did that which was right in his own eyes.*"

(Gen..... ....)
"*In the beginning God...*"

Changing Starting Points

> The real argument is down at the starting point level. How can we get the other person to change their starting point? We can't!

> We can't raise the dead; we can't save ourselves; we can't change our starting point.

> Only God can save us. It's only a work of the Holy Spirit on their hearts that can change their starting point.

I am often asked how people change their biases. This is a good question. As a Christian, the only way I can answer is to say that in this area it has to be a work of the Holy Spirit. The Bible teaches that we walk either in the light or in darkness (Acts 26:18), gather or scatter, are for Christ or against Him (Matt. 12:30). The Bible clearly declares that no person is neutral and that each one does have a bias. Since it is the Holy Spirit who convicts and convinces people of the truth, it is only through the work of the Holy Spirit that our biases can change. As Christians, our job is to bring the Word of God to people in a clear and gracious way, and pray that the Spirit might use our words to open hearts and minds to Christ. I believe Christians understand bias better than others. All Christians were once lost sinners biased against God. They have seen how Jesus Christ can change their bias as He transforms their lives through the power of His Spirit. (Ken Ham, *The Lie: Evolution*, chapter 1)

> We use everything we can to convince them of the truth, to answer their skeptical questions, to point out their logical fallacies, but always in the context of the Word of God, and then we stand back and leave the rest to God. Only He can open their minds to the truth.

> When the starting point in America was God's Word, the worldview permeated the culture. Marriage— one man for one woman. Abortion was considered murder, and so on. There's right, and there's wrong, and there's good, and there's bad.

> So many church leaders have adopted the pagan religion of the age— man's ideas to explain life without God, evolution, millions of years, man's fallible ideas—into God's Word, contaminated God's Word, and undermined the authority of the Word. We're losing the next generation and not affecting the culture.

> We've been ashamed of the Word of God; we've given up our starting point. We need to honor God's Word, and stand up for what's right. God will honor those who honor Him.

> We need to unashamedly, uncompromisingly stand on the authority of the Word!

Group Discussion Questions

1. What are some problems with the Intelligent Design Movement?

2. Should we leave the Bible out of our arguments regarding creation vs. evolution, abortion, and gay marriage? Why or why not?

3. How does one's starting point influence his worldview? What is the only correct starting point?

4. According to the following Scriptures, what are some reasons people don't believe in God?

    • Jeremiah 17:9 –

    • 2 Corinthians 4:4 –

    • Romans 1:18–19 –

For Personal Reflection

1. Do you use the Word of God when witnessing to others? Do you realize that your words are not powerful, but God's Word is?

2. Do you know the Word of God? Have you memorized Scripture so that you are ready to share it with others and see God use it in their lives?

For Next Week

Please read and meditate on the following verses in preparation for next week's lesson:

- 1 Corinthians 1:18–25
- Acts 2:14–39
- Acts 17:16–34

For Further Study

- Fool-Proof Apologetics – www.answersingenesis.org/articles/am/v4/n2/fool-proof
- Apologetics Web Series – www.answersingenesis.org/get-answers/k/apologetics-series/v/recent
- Get Answers – www.answersingenesis.org/get-answers

Resources

- *Ultimate Apologetics* DVD series, featuring Jason Lisle, Answers in Genesis
- *Apologetics Classroom* DVD Series, featuring Mike Riddle, Creation Training Initiative
- *Always Ready*, Greg Bahnsen, Covenant Media Press

Lesson 5: Revealing the Unknown God – Part 1

Objectives

It is our prayer that after you have finished these lessons you will be able to . . .

- Describe the essential elements of the gospel.
- Recognize the foundational change that has occurred in our culture.

Introduction

"But we preach Christ crucified, to the Jews a stumbling block and to the Greeks foolishness" (1 Corinthians 1:23).

A tremendous example of successful evangelism is Peter's sermon on the Day of Pentecost, in Acts 2. Peter boldly preached the message of the Cross and the Resurrection, and thousands were saved.

The people who heard his message had an Old Testament background. They believed in the Creator God and understood sin and its penalty of death. When Peter was preaching to the Jews, it was like building a house, knowing that the foundation was already there. He could go straight to the structure to be built on the foundation.

In Acts 17:18–34, however, Paul preached to a totally different culture. Paul was speaking to the Greek philosophers. They had a different understanding compared to the Jews.

1. The Greek culture had no concept of a personal, infinite God who was responsible for, transcendent to, and an upholder of His creation.

2. The Greeks did not have the Scriptures. While they saw "sin" and "evil" and recognized the importance of laws, they had no concept of an absolute authority, absolute truth, or the inherent sin nature of man.

3. The Greeks had no understanding concerning their first ancestor, Adam, and original sin—nor had they received the Law of Moses. So these people could not understand or accept the absolute authority of the Creator God, the Lawgiver.

How could Paul get them to understand?

Paul knew that he could appeal to nature and their consciences to explain the concept of the true Creator God (Romans 1:20, 2:15). So Paul explained the Christian message from the foundation upwards. Paul pointed to one of their own altars that they had inscribed to the "unknown god." He explained this unknown god was in reality the true God. He urged them to repent from their erroneous ways and believe in the true God.

Finally, once they understood creation and our descent from the first man, Adam, Paul turned to the message of the Resurrection, the central part of the gospel.

Generations ago in nations like America and England, evangelists could assume a foundation upon which the gospel could stand. However, there has been a major change—and the church has sadly missed it.

(From "The Cross—Stumbling Block or Foolishness?" by Ken Ham, *Answers*, Oct–Dec, 2010).

Video Viewing Guide

› In our Western culture, people are not responding to the gospel today as they have in the past. Why is that? Our Western world has lost its biblical worldview; the culture has changed.

› There are really only two religions in the world: God's Word or man's word.

> On the basis of those two different religions we have two different worldviews. One is a worldview of Christian absolutes; the other is a worldview of moral relativism.

> Our country's starting point was the Bible. That's why a Christian worldview permeated this culture.

> But we've had generations now, right throughout our Western world, that have been told the history in the Bible, particularly in Genesis 1–11, is not true. Subsequent generations have started to recognize that if that history in Genesis is not true, then neither is the gospel based in that history.

> The secularists have attacked God's Word. God's Word has come under attack since Genesis 3. But in this era of history, it's particularly been in Genesis 1–11.

> Much of the church has even said we don't really need that part of the Bible, or it doesn't matter. You don't have to take it as literal history.

> The moral "problems" in our culture are in essence the symptoms of the problem. The secularists captured generations of hearts and minds, changed their hearts and minds in regard to what they believe about the Word of God—to believe it's man that should be the starting point. That's changed their worldview, which changed the culture.

Cultures in the West were once pervaded by a primarily Christian worldview because the majority of people at least respected the Bible as the authority on morality. It needs to be clearly understood that over the past 200 years the Bible's authority has been increasingly undermined, as much of the Church has compromised with the idea of millions of years (this began before Darwin) and has thus begun reinterpreting Genesis. When those outside the Church saw Church leaders rejecting Genesis as literal history, one can understand why they would have quickly lost respect for all of the Bible.

The Bible has lost respect in people's eyes (both within and without the Church) to the extent that the culture as a whole now does not take the Bible's morality seriously at all. The increasing acceptance of homosexual behavior and gay marriage is a symptom of the loss of biblical authority, and is primarily due to the compromise the Church has made with the secular world's teaching on origins. (Ken Ham, "How Should a Christian Respond to 'Gay Marriage,'" *The New Answers Book 2*)

› The church has tried to change the culture, but we are not called to change the culture, but preach the gospel.

> We should have been raising up generations standing on the authority of the Word of God, who knew how to defend the faith, who would be the salt and light in the culture.

> What is the gospel? The good news that Jesus Christ died on a cross and was raised from the dead.

> But isn't it also true that you can't understand the good news of the gospel unless you understand the bad news in Genesis? The bad news concerning a perfect world marred by sin. That the first man, Adam, rebelled, and thus sin came into the world, and thus death as a consequence.

> That's why we need a Savior. That's why Jesus Christ stepped into history. In other words, the history in Genesis 1–11 is foundational to understanding the Good News.

> The gospel has three aspects:

1. Foundational knowledge –

2. Power –

3. Hope –

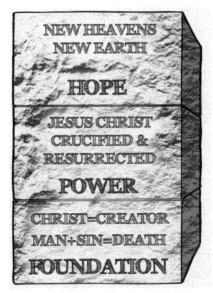

> Most of the church around the world concentrates mainly on the power and the hope of the gospel, not the foundational aspects.

> People in the church seem more interested in end times than in the beginning. There are many churches, to become a member of the church, you have to agree to a particular view of eschatology for that particular church. But when it comes to Genesis, you can believe in millions of years, evolution, it doesn't matter, as long as you believe God created.

> The reason that people have different views of Genesis is because they're starting outside of the Bible with the secular views of this age, and reinterpreting Genesis, and coming up with those different positions to impose the idea of millions of years onto the Bible.

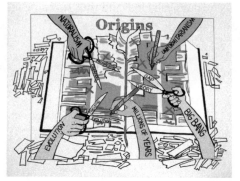

A Foundational Change

> 1 Corinthians 1:23 – But we preach Christ crucified, unto the Jews a stumbling block, but unto the Greeks foolishness.

> In Acts 2, Peter, on the day of Pentecost, preached a very powerful sermon, and 3,000 souls were saved.

> We used to see crusades like that. We used to see evangelistic campaigns like that. We've seen great revivals in America, in the East in the past, and other places. There have been great revivals in the past. Over in England, and across the United Kingdom, and other places in Europe, there have been times when there have been great revivals. But we don't see those sorts of things today.

> Most of what we do in our churches today—our evangelistic campaigns, even our Easter pageants, Christmas pageants, our Sunday school material, Bible study material, youth group material, whatever it is—is basically an Acts 2 approach to evangelism.

> Peter was preaching to mainly Jews. He didn't have to define God. He didn't have to define sin. They had the right starting point, which put them on the right road, but their stumbling block was the message of the Cross.

> In Acts 17 when Paul went to Mars Hill, Athens, and he met there with the Greek philosophers and he preached unto them Jesus and the Resurrection, what was the response? The response was, "Foolishness!"

> Paul was he preaching to Greek philosophers here. The Epicureans believed that everything evolved from the earth, that sensuous pleasure was the chief good of existence, and so on. They were evolutionists. The Stoics were pantheists. Pantheism is another form of evolutionism. That culture had no foundation to understand the gospel.

Group Discussion Questions

1. How are differing views of eschatology different from differing views of Genesis & creation?

2. Discuss instances where you have tried to communicate something to someone, but they couldn't understand what you were trying to tell them because of their cultural background difference.

3. Three elements of the gospel are prerequisite to understanding how the gospel should be presented to different people within a culture (or in different cultures). What are they, and which do you think is most important?

4. Why was the preaching of the Cross considered a "stumbling block" to the Jews?

5. Why was the preaching of the Cross considered "foolishness" to the Greeks?

For Personal Reflection

1. Have you witnessed to anyone lately? If your answer is no, why not?

2. What steps can you take to become more equipped to share the gospel, and then to step out and do so?

For Next Week

Please read and meditate on the following verses in preparation for next week's lesson:

- 1 Peter 3:13–17
- 1 Thessalonians 2:1–13
- 2 Corinthians 4:1–6

For Further Study

- Evangelism in Pagan World – www.answersingenesis.org/articles/lie/evangelism-pagan-world
- From Jews to Greeks – www.answersingenesis.org/Home/Area/wwtl/chapter7.asp
- How Can I Use This Information to Witness? – www.answersingenesis.org/articles/nab/how-use-information-to-witness

Resources

- *Why Won't They Listen?* by Ken Ham, Master Books
- *The New Answers Books*, volumes 1–3, edited by Ken Ham, Master Books
- *The Ultimate Proof of Creation* by Jason Lisle, Master Books

Lesson 6: Revealing the Unknown God – Part 2

Objectives

It is our prayer that after you have finished these lessons you will be able to . . .

- Define the difference between an Acts 2 culture and an Acts 17 culture.
- Recognize the key to changing the culture.

Introduction

Over the years, both in Australia and in America, I've had a number of Bible college and seminary students relate to me what some of their professors had declared concerning Paul's sermon in Acts 17. These professors said that Paul really failed in his approach at Athens because there were so few converts. He had tried to be too intellectual. What Paul should have done, they argued, was just boldly preach the message of sin and repentance as Peter did in Acts 2. The professors instructed the students not to adopt Paul's approach at Athens, but instead always pattern their evangelistic efforts after Peter's, outlined in Acts 2.

In actual fact, Paul was very successful in his Acts 17 sermon. Many people have missed the point that Paul was preaching to a culture that had the wrong foundation to understand the gospel. To communicate with such a culture, Paul had to change a whole way of thinking from the ground up. It wasn't just a matter of presenting the message of the Cross and Resurrection; these people had to be given a whole new way to think before they could understand such a message.

I can't emphasize enough the enormity of the task Paul had in communicating the truth of the gospel to the Greek culture. To understand more of what Paul had to do, we could liken Paul's work to that of a pioneer.

When the pioneers moved westward across America, they couldn't just set up camp, plant some seeds, and then reap a harvest. They first of all had to clear the land, then prepare the soil, plant the seed, and then they could obtain a harvest.

Consider the well-known parable of the sower and the seed in Matthew 13:3–8. It was only when the seed fell in good ground that it could then bring forth fruit. When Paul went to the Greeks to sow the seed of the gospel, it was like sowing seeds by the wayside or on stony ground. Before the Greeks could understand the gospel, Paul had to prepare the ground—he had to construct the right foundation so the seed of the gospel could take root. Before he could successfully sow the seed, he first had to plow the ground!

What Paul was involved in was pre-evangelism (or what I call "creation evangelism"). Mostly, we think of evangelism as sowing and reaping. Perhaps a pastor in a church sows the seed week after week, and then an evangelist is brought in and a harvest of souls is reaped. This, of course, works when the ground is already prepared to receive the seed as it was with the Jews. Christians, however, need to become familiar with the fact that it is becoming increasingly necessary to be involved in plowing first, then sowing, and finally reaping.

Many Christians have not thought about the concept of pioneer evangelism (or pre-evangelism). Or if they have, they usually think of this method as reserved for overseas missionaries ministering to some tribe of native people in a remote jungle.

As we shall see in this session, however, pioneer evangelism must be adopted by the church today, or there will be little plowed ground left for sowing the seed of the gospel. This is a necessary consequence of a foundational cultural change that has occurred in our Western nations. Did the church miss this change? By and large, yes—because the church, sadly, has actually helped bring this about!

(From *Why Won't They Listen?* by Ken Ham, chapter 6)

Video Viewing Guide

> Generations ago, our Western world was primarily an Acts 2–type culture one way or another. And so evangelists could come in and preach the message of the cross and people would understand.

> America's no longer an Acts 2 culture; it's increasingly an Acts 17 culture. It's thrown creation, Bible, prayer out of the public schools.

> The Greeks were on a whole different road—a whole different starting point, a whole different worldview. That road does not lead up to the message of the Cross. And if you want that Greek to understand the message of the Cross, you realize you've got to do something. You've got to get him off the wrong road and give him a whole new starting point—give him the right history, the right foundation; get him on the right road that will lead up to the message of the Cross.

> Do you know what Paul had to do? Using the terms Greeks and Jews as types, he had to turn Greeks into Jews. He was preaching to people who had the wrong foundation.

> Our culture is much more like the Greeks. Whole generations brought up in an education system devoid of the knowledge of God. If anything, Christianity—the Bible—is taught against, mocked, scoffed, openly mocked in our culture. They're taught about many gods, and you preach the message of the Cross, and it's foolishness unto them.

> We're no longer an Acts 2 culture. We're an Acts 17 culture. Whole generations of kids now are going to the Greek schools. They've thrown God, the Bible, prayer; they threw Christianity out and replaced it with the religion of naturalism.

> What we're doing as a church through our Sunday school literature, Bible study literature, evangelistic campaigns, our Bible tracts, our Easter pageants, Christmas pageants—through most of our thrust as a church, we're not approaching them as Greeks; we're approaching them as Jews.

> You know 1 Peter 3:15? Always be prepared to give a defense or to give an answer? We're not teaching apologetics. The Greeks are teaching our kids apologetics. They're teaching them, "Here's the reasons to believe in millions of years. Here's the reasons to believe in evolution. Here's all the reasons the Bible's not true." What do we do? "Here's the stories. Trust in Jesus." The Greeks are changing their foundation from God's Word to man's word, and what are we doing? "Oh, that's OK. You can believe in that. Trust in Jesus."

> Generations of our kids, a whole culture, all of us are being Greekized, and we need to de-Greekize. We need to be taking people off the wrong road and giving them the right starting point, putting them on the right road so they'll understand the message of the Cross.

> Generations ago, there was lot of plowed ground ready for the seed—plowed by the churches, homes, schools. So a sower would come and when he threw out the seed of the gospel, it could take root, like it did in Acts 2.

The enemy, however, has sown seeds of destruction. Much of the plowed ground is now covered with the trees of evolutionary biology and the rocks of evolutionary geology. Although there is still some plowed ground, it is disappearing at an alarming rate. Many of the younger generations are coming through an education system that has trained them in an anti-Christian philosophy.

In a sense, I picture the "creation evangelist" as one who is using a bulldozer to plow the ground, first to rid it of rocks, trees, and debris that have prevented the seed from taking root. Evolution is one of the biggest, if not the biggest, stumbling block to people listening to the gospel today. This stumbling block must be removed. The enemy has taken over the territory, and we need to claim it back. Plowing the ground and preparing the foundation—that's what "creation evangelism" is all about. (Ken Ham, *Why Won't They Listen?*, chapter 9)

> But now those same churches, schools, homes have actually allowed the enemy to come in and sow in seeds of destruction. And now the plowed ground has by and large disappeared and become clouded by the rocks of evolutionary geology and the trees of evolutionary biology.

> We have got to be pioneer evangelists to get the ground ready again so the seed can take root and there can be a harvest.

Group Discussion Questions

1. What assumptions could Peter make about his audience when he preached in Acts 2?

2. With whom was Paul communicating in Acts 17? What were their beliefs (about God, evolution, and Christ)?

3. Why couldn't Paul reason with his audience from Scripture (as Peter had in Acts 2)?

4. How can we de-Greekize ourselves, our families, and our churches?

For Personal Reflection

1. How have you or your family been affected by the foundational shift in our culture?

2. What can you do to de-Greekize yourself and your family?

3. How might you change your approach to evangelism based on what Ken shared?

For Next Week

Please read and meditate on the following verses in preparation for next week's lesson:

- Genesis 1:1–31
- 2 Peter 3:1–13
- Proverbs 30:5–6

For Further Study

- Evangelism in a Pagan World – www.answersingenesis.org/articles/2007/01/04/evangelism-pagan-world
- From Jews to Greeks – www.answersingenesis.org/Home/Area/wwtl/chapter7.asp
- How Can I Use This Information to Witness? – www.answersingenesis.org/articles/nab/how-use-information-to-witness

Resources

- *Why Won't They Listen?* by Ken Ham, Master Books
- *The New Answers Books*, volumes 1–3, edited by Ken Ham, Master Books
- *The Ultimate Proof of Creation* by Jason Lisle, Master Books

Lesson 7: In Six Days - Part 1

Objectives

It is our prayer that after you have finished these lessons you will be able to . . .

- Explain why the Hebrew word *yom* in the context of Genesis 1 means an ordinary, normal-length day.

- Understand how many in the church have brought in outside influences and reinterpreted the days of Genesis 1.

Introduction

If the days of creation are really geologic ages of millions of years, then the gospel message is undermined at its foundation because it puts death, disease, and suffering *before* the Fall. The effort to define "days" as "geologic ages" results from an erroneous approach to Scripture—reinterpreting the Word of God on the basis of the fallible theories of sinful people.

It is a good exercise to read Genesis 1 and try to put aside outside influences that may cause you to have a predetermined idea of what the word "day" may mean. Just let the words of the passage speak to you.

Taking Genesis 1 in this way, at face value, without doubt it says that God created the universe, the earth, the sun, moon and stars, plants and animals, and the first two people within six ordinary (approximately 24-hour) days. Being really honest, you would have to admit that you could never get the idea of millions of years from reading this passage.

The majority of Christians (including many Christian leaders) in the Western world, however, do not insist that these days of creation were ordinary-length days, and many of them accept and teach, based on outside influences, that they must have been long periods of time—even millions or billions of years.

(From "Could God Really Have Created Everything in Six Days?" by Ken Ham in *The New Answers Book 1*)

Video Viewing Guide

> Exodus 20:11 "For in six days the LORD made the heavens and the earth, the sea, and all that is in them, and rested the seventh day."

> Proverbs 30:5–6 "Every word of God is pure; He is a shield to those who put their trust in Him. Do not add to His words, lest He rebuke you, and you be found a liar."

> The secular world doesn't really care so much if Christian leaders believe in evolution. They don't really care as much about that. But you know what they really care about and get really emotional about? If you don't believe in billions of years. You know why that is? You have to have an incomprehensible amount of time to even postulate the idea of evolution.

> Where do we get the idea of just a few thousand years for the age of the earth? Well, if you take those days as ordinary days, as ordinary 24-hour days, and you start adding up those genealogies in the Bible. From Adam and Abraham about 2,000 years, and then from Abraham to today 4,000 years. That's where we get the 6,000 years from.

> From 30 years' experience in this ministry, the majority of Christian leaders, the majority of pastors, the majority of Christian college professors, seminary professors, Bible college professors; the majority of Christians in our churches—elders, deacons—will not take a stand on six literal days.

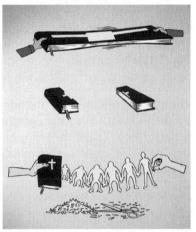

> The Hebrew word for day—*yom*—is used in the singular and plural form 2,301 times in the Old Testament. The Hebrew word day can have a number of different meanings just like the English word day.

> If we just look at the meaning of the word *yom* in the Old Testament outside of Genesis 1, here's what we find:

  • The Hebrew word for day with a number occurs 410 times, and always means an ordinary day.

  • The phrase "evening and morning" occurs 38 times, and always means an ordinary day.

  • The word "evening" with "day," or "morning" with "day," occurs 23 times, and always means an ordinary day.

  • The word "night" with "day" occurs 52 times, and always means an ordinary day.

> Do you realize if the word day was written like that anywhere else in the Old Testament, you would not even question what it meant? It means an ordinary day. It's so obvious.

> When Moses writes that God created Heaven and Earth and whatever is in them in six days, then let this period continue to have been six days, and do not venture to devise any comment according to which six days were one day. But, if you cannot understand how this could have been done in six days, then grant the Holy Spirit the honor of being more learned than you are. (Martin Luther)

> Well, if it's so obvious that they're six ordinary days, why don't many Christians or Christian leaders believe the days in Genesis 1 are literal 24-hour days? And I'll tell you why it is. It has nothing to do ultimately with what the Bible so obviously tells us. It has everything to do with trying to fit millions of years into the Bible.

> I go to churches and they say, "Oh, our pastor believes in theistic evolution." "Our pastor believes in the Day-Age Theory." "We have deacons who believe in a local flood." "Our Sunday school teacher believes in progressive creation." "We have people at our church that believe in the Gap Theory." Not one of these positions comes from the Bible; they're all imposed on the Bible. They all have one common factor—the millions of years.

> The Days of Creation were ordinary days in length. We must understand that these days were actual days, contrary to the opinion of the Holy Fathers. Whenever we observe that the opinions of the Fathers disagree with Scripture, we reverently bear with them and acknowledge them to be our elders. Nevertheless, we do not depart from the authority of Scripture for their sake. (Martin Luther)

Group Discussion Questions

1. Why is not believing the millions of years an even bigger deal than not believing evolution?

2. How can we determine the age of the earth?

3. Why does 2 Peter 3:8—"A day is like a thousand years"—have nothing to do with the length of the days of creation?

4. How do we know the days mentioned in Genesis 1 refer to normal-length days and not long periods of time?

5. If it is so obvious that the days in Genesis 1 are normal-length days, then why don't many Christian scholars accept them as literal days?

For Personal Reflection

1. How have you been influenced by secular arguments, maybe even unwittingly?

2. Are you spending time daily in God's Word so that you know what it says, and can you teach it to others and defend it from skeptics? If not, how can you plan to do so?

For Next Week

Please read and meditate on the following verses in preparation for next week's lesson:

- Mark 10:1–12
- Genesis 3:1–6
- Genesis 1:29–30, 9:1–3

For Further Study

- Does Radiometric Dating Prove the Earth Is Old? – www.answersingenesis.org/articles/nab/does-radiometric-dating-prove
- Could God have Created in Six Days? – www.answersingenesis.org/articles/nab/could-god-have-created-in-six-days
- Unlocking the Truth of Scripture – www.answersingenesis.org/articles/am/v2/n4/unlocking-scripture
- Did Jesus Say He Created in Six Literal Days? – www.answersingenesis.org/articles/nab/did-jesus-say-he-created-in-six-days
- Six Literal Days – www.answersingenesis.org/articles/am/v5/n2/six-literal-days

Resources

- *In Six Days*, John F. Ashton, editor, Master Books
- *The Six Days of Genesis*, Paul F. Taylor, Day One Publishing
- *The New Answers Book 1*, Ken Ham, general editor, Master Books

Lesson 8: In Six Days - Part 2

Objectives

It is our prayer that after you have finished these lessons you will be able to . . .

- Explain how radiometric dating methods do not support an old age for the earth.
- Explain the theological importance of believing in six literal days of creation.

Introduction

God's Word unmistakably teaches a young earth and universe ("the heavens"). God has ensured the accurate recording and preservation of His eyewitness account of the earth's history, which Jesus Christ endorsed repeatedly during His earthly ministry.

God took great care to include the necessary chronological details of the universe's creation in six literal days, as well as the unbroken genealogies of mankind from Adam to Jesus. So we have absolutely no doubt that the earth is only around six thousand years old.

Contrary to Scripture, many geologists claim that radiometric "clocks" show rocks to be millions of years old. However, to read any clock accurately we must know where the clock was set at the beginning. It's like making sure that an hourglass clock was set with all the sand in the top bowl at the beginning. However, no geologists were present when the earth and its many rock layers were formed, so they cannot know where the radiometric clocks were set at the beginning.

Also, we have to be sure that the clock has ticked at the same rate from the beginning until now. No geologists have been observing the radiometric clocks for millions of years to check that the rate of radioactive decay has always been the same as the rate today. To the contrary, we now have impeccable evidence that radioactive decay rates were greatly sped up at some point during the past, for example, during the global catastrophic Genesis Flood.

God is beyond time, which He created. He has told us when He created everything and thus how old the universe is. So we finite humans should fearlessly embrace His testimony of a young earth, recorded in His inerrant Word.

(From "Radiometric Dating" by Andrew Snelling, *Answers*, Jan–Mar, 2010)

Video Viewing Guide

> Mark 10:6 "But from the beginning of creation, God 'made them male and female.'" Do you realize if the beginning was 15 billion years before male and female were on the earth, that doesn't make any sense? But if the beginning was just a few days before He made male and female, that makes a lot of sense.

Dating Methods

> When something looks like it contradicts the Bible, you make sure you go to the Bible. You make sure you look at the context; make sure you look at the literature; make sure you're understanding it correctly. And if you're sure of what it's saying and there's still that contradiction, you don't question God's Word, you question fallible man's word.

> There are actually hundreds of dating methods that you can use to age-date things on the earth. For a dating method, you need something that changes with time, then you have to know something about how it started—what was there to start with—and how it's changed over time, and to be sure of what happened so you can figure out how long it's been going on. But does anyone see some problems there? We weren't there when it started and we weren't there to check it over all those years.

The assumptions on which the radioactive dating is based are not only unprovable but plagued with problems. Rocks may have inherited parent and daughter isotopes from their sources, or they may have been contaminated when they moved through other rocks to their current locations. Or inflowing water may have mixed isotopes into the rocks. In addition, the radioactive decay rates have not been constant.

So if these clocks are based on faulty assumptions and yield unreliable results, then scientists should not trust or promote the claimed radioactive "ages" of countless millions of years, especially since they contradict the true history of the universe as recorded in God's Word. (Andrew Snelling, "Radiometric Dating: Problems with the Assumptions," *Answers*, Jul–Sep, 2009)

› Of all the dating methods you can use to age-date things on the earth, 90% of them actually contradict billions of years. Only 10% give the billions of years.

› When they used the potassium-argon dating method to date the basalt, it dated to 45 million years old. When they used carbon dating to date the wood, it dated to 45,000 years old. 45,000-year-old wood in 45-million-year-old basalt. There's a problem.

› If something is millions of years old, you shouldn't find carbon-14 in it, but actually, we do. We find it in dinosaur bones and coal deposits and so on said to be millions of years old.

Can a Christian Believe in Millions of Years?

› In Genesis 1:29–30 God told Adam and Eve to eat fruit, that the animals were going to be vegetarian. It wasn't until Genesis 9:3 that God said that we could eat meat.

> If you believe in millions of years as a Christian, you believe that the fossil record was laid down millions of years before man because that's what the secular world is telling us. But the fossil record's not just a record of death. It's a record of death; it's a record of disease; it's a record of animals eating each other.

> But God said everything He made was very good. How could He call cancer, brain tumors, very good?

> When you take God's perfect Word and man's fallible opinion, when people try to make them agree, which one usually gets modified? The Bible.

› There's been an attack on God's Word ever since Genesis 3, but in our era of history, the attack has particularly been on Genesis 1–11. And I believe the days of creation and the millions of years, that's one of the greatest attacks on the authority of Scripture in our age.

› The issue of the age of the earth is not a salvation issue because salvation is not conditioned upon what you believe about the age of the earth. But it is an authority issue.

› If we don't take God at His Word and we allow outside ideas to then reinterpret God's Word, we have undermined the authority from which we get the gospel.

Group Discussion Questions

1. How does Mark 10:6 support the idea of a young earth?

2. What are some theological reasons the earth cannot be millions of years old?

3.   What are some of the problems with radiometric dating?

For Personal Reflection

1.   There is no biblical or scientific reason to be ashamed of believing in a recent six-day creation. Have you ever been ashamed to admit that you are a biblical creationist?

2.   In what ways have you allowed men's opinions to shape your belief in the Word of God? Do you trust it fully from beginning to end?

For Next Week

Please read and meditate on the following verses in preparation for next week's lesson:

- Acts 17:24–27
- Genesis 5:1–5
- Genesis 11:1–9

For Further Study

- Does Radiometric Dating Prove the Earth Is Old? – www. answersingenesis.org/articles/nab/does-radiometric-dating-prove
- Could God Have Created in Six Days? – www.answersingenesis.org/ articles/nab/could-god-have-created-in-six-days
- Did Jesus Say He Created in Six Literal Days? – www. answersingenesis.org/articles/nab/did-jesus-say-he-created-in-six-days
- Six Literal Days – www.answersingenesis.org/articles/am/v5/n2/ six-literal-days

Resources

- *In Six Days*, John F. Ashton, editor, Master Books
- *The Six Days of Genesis*, Paul F. Taylor, Day One Publishing
- *The New Answers Book 1*, Ken Ham, general editor, Master Books

Lesson 9: One Blood, One Race – Part 1

Objectives

It is our prayer that after you have finished these lessons you will be able to . . .

- Answer the question, "Where did Cain get his wife?"
- Explain how the various people groups arose after the dispersion at the Tower of Babel.

Introduction

In the mid-1800s, as the sailing ship *Beagle* cut through the oceans, a theologian and amateur biologist was formulating an idea. Without the insight of modern-day genetics and supported by superficial observations, his ideas began to solidify into a theory: the theory of evolution. In his history-altering book, *The Origin of the Species*, Charles Darwin conceptualized a world where life spontaneously came into being and then changed over time by the forces of nature into the phenomenal complexity and diversity of life we now see on this planet.

Like a seed, the idea was firmly planted in Charles's mind, where it began to grow and mature. Through his writings and lectures, the seed then became planted in the minds of others. Soon the theory had taken root in the gardens of the scientific community. Blown by the winds of society, the idea of evolution found its way into the fields of the education systems of the young. Its seeds spread into the laws of government. Soon enough, its roots began to infiltrate the mind of the Church, where it began to choke out the faith many held in the Word of God. In time, this single idea overtook almost the entire plantation of Western thinking.

It didn't take long for the fruit of this plantation to begin to ripen. Nowhere has this been more obvious than in the area of racism. While Darwin himself probably never imagined the impact his idea would have on the culturally diverse peoples of the earth, history has shown us how evolutionary thought fuels racism and how racists use evolution to justify their hatred for those who are different than they are.

Evolutionists like Hitler treated the Jews, Gypsies, and other groups as inferior. He therefore argued that they needed to be eliminated. Today, depending on the country, marriages between different people groups often result in persecution for the parents and the children. Current attempts at "ethnic cleansing" are the result of hatred of one particular people group toward another. Even within segments of the Church, intense prejudice can be seen toward those whose skin is of a different shade.

All of these problems and many others concerning racism and prejudice could easily be solved if new seeds of truth from God's Word (properly interpreted alongside scientific fact) were planted and cultivated in our minds.

(From *One Blood, One Race* by Ken Ham & A. Charles Ware, introduction)

Video Viewing Guide

Where Did Cain Get His Wife?

› In 1 Corinthians 15:45, Paul tells us "the first man Adam"—there's one man, Adam. Genesis 3:20, Eve was given that name because she was to be the mother of all the living—not some of the living, all the living. It's very obvious from Scripture that there was one man, one woman to start with—Adam and Eve.

› In Acts 17:26, Paul said God "made from one blood every nation of men to dwell on all the face of the earth." We're all related. We all go back to one man, one woman.

› Genesis 5:4 says Adam "had sons and daughters." If there's Adam and Eve and they had sons and daughters—only one man and one woman to start with. And if marriage is one man for one woman, which is what the Bible clearly teaches, then originally, brothers married sisters.

Can Close Relatives Marry?

› When God made Adam and Eve, they were perfect. Everything was very good. But Adam sinned. So God withdrew some of His sustaining power so now the whole universe runs down, we run down, and we die. Our body dies. You see, because God no longer holds everything together perfectly, there are mutations— mistakes, copying mistakes—from one generation to the next and they keep accumulating more and more over time.

› If you're closely related, you're more likely to inherit the similar mistakes from your parents. And if those mistakes get together when the sperm fertilizes the egg, there's an increased likelihood of deformities—problems in the offspring.

› The further back in history you go towards Adam and Eve, there will be fewer and fewer mistakes. Adam and Eve were perfect. Their children wouldn't have had that many mistakes; it wouldn't have been a problem for brother to marry sister provided it was one man for one woman.

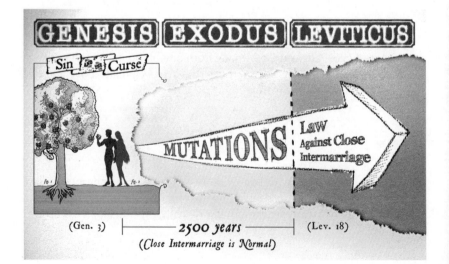

Where Did the "Races" Come From?

> If we are all descendants of Adam and Eve, then how many races are there? Only one!

> When you read Genesis chapter 1, the Bible tells us that God created the animals and plants after their kind. The Bible's not saying animals don't change. It's just saying each kind is going to produce its own kind.

> From a Darwinian evolution perspective, the secularists believe we start with no information, matter, that somehow produces a language system and information—DNA. And over millions of years, you get zillions of bits of new information to produce bigger and bigger pools of information to get all the different kinds of animals and plants.

> The Bible tells us God made the kinds to start with, so He made the big pools of information to start with and what we observe over time is redistribution of information and a loss of information, the opposite of evolution.

> God made Adam and Eve, and then by the time of the Flood there are eight people that survived on Noah's ark—Noah and his family. And they came off the Ark and numbers increased again. Well, how would we get distinct people groups with distinguishing characteristics like the American Indians, Fijians, Hawaiians, Eskimos, Australian Aborigines—people groups that have dark skin, people groups with light skin, and so on? Something in history would have to split up the human gene pool. Is there anything you can think of in human history that could split up the human gene pool? The Tower of Babel.

> Language barriers separated and isolated the people, causing different people groups to arise.

The Bible does not even use the word *race* in reference to people, but it does describe all human beings as being of "one blood" (Acts 17:26). This of course emphasizes that we are all related, as all humans are descendants of the first man, Adam (1 Corinthians 15:45), who was created in the image of God (Genesis 1:26–27). The Last Adam, Jesus Christ (1 Corinthians 15:45) also became a descendant of Adam. Any descendant of Adam can be saved because our mutual relative by blood (Jesus Christ) died and rose again. This is why the gospel can (and should) be preached to all tribes and nations. (Ken Ham, "Are There Really Different Races?" *The New Answers Book 1*)

Evolutionary Ideas Fueled Racism

> In 1859 Charles Darwin published a book entitled On the Origin of Species by Means of Natural Selection or the Preservation of Favored Races in the Struggle for Life.

> The late Stephen J. Gould from Harvard University made this statement: "Biological arguments for racism may have been common before 1850, but they increased by orders of magnitude following the acceptance of evolutionary theory."

> Evolution is not the cause of racism; sin is the cause of racism. But when you're taught an idea that there are lower races and higher races and primitive races, and you think you might be one of the advanced races, you could see how you could actually feel a type of racism and prejudice.

Group Discussion Questions

1. How would you answer the question, "Where did Cain get his wife?"

2. Why was it not a problem for close relatives to marry originally, but it is now?

3.   Is natural selection the same thing as evolution? Explain.

4.   Why is it incorrect to say, "God created all the species that we have today"?

5.   Can you explain how all the different people groups arose?

For Personal Reflection

1.   Describe, in your own words, why racist attitudes are wrong, according to the Bible. What should our attitudes be toward different people groups?

2. Have you experienced prejudice based on external characteristics? How did it make you feel?

3. Have you ever treated anyone with racial prejudice? Do you know others who hold prejudicial views? How could you battle those wrong ideas?

For Next Week

Please read and meditate on the following verses in preparation for next week's lesson:

- 2 Corinthians 6:14–16
- Malachi 2:10–17
- 1 Samuel 16:4–12

For Further Study

- Are There Really Different Races? – www.answersingenesis.org/articles/nab/are-there-different-races
- One Race, One Blood – www.answersingenesis.org/articles/orob
- Get Answers: Racism – www.answersingenesis.org/get-answers/topic/racism

Resources

- *One Blood, One Race* by Ken Ham and A. Charles Ware
- *All God's Children* by Ken Ham

Lesson 10: One Blood, One Race – Part 2

Objectives

It is our prayer that after you have finished these lessons you will be able to . . .

- Describe how genetics explains the variations among various people groups.
- Recognize that all people are related.

Introduction

Some people think there must be different races of people because there appear to be major differences between various groups, such as skin color and eye shape.

The truth, though, is that these so-called "racial characteristics" are only minor variations among people groups. If one were to take any two people anywhere in the world, scientists have found that the basic genetic differences between these two people would typically be around 0.2 percent—even if they came from the same people group. But these so-called "racial" characteristics that people think are major differences (skin color, eye shape, etc.) account for only 0.012 percent of human biological variation.

In other words, the so-called "racial" differences are absolutely trivial—overall, there is more variation within any group than there is between one group and another. If a white person is looking for a tissue match for an organ transplant, for instance, the best match may come from a black person, and vice versa.

The only reason many people think these differences are major is because they've been brought up in a culture that has taught them to see the differences this way.

According to the Bible's history, all humans are descendants of Adam and Eve—thus only one biological race exists. All humans in the world today are classified as *Homo sapiens sapiens* (same genus, species, and subspecies). When the Human Genome Project published a draft of their findings in 2000, the *New York Times* reported that "the researchers had unanimously declared there is only one race—the human race."

To form different people groups with distinguishing characteristics, one would need to split up the human population and isolate groups from each other. The Tower of Babel, as recorded in Genesis 11, provides the historical basis for the formation of such people groups. There is so much information in the human genome that zillions of combinations are possible.

Yet all humans basically have the same skin color—a brown pigment called *melanin*. Although there are a couple of forms of melanin and other pigments and factors playing minor roles in skin color, every human basically has a brown color.

Lots of brown is called black, and a little brown color is called white. In actuality, no human really is "black" and no human is "white." There are not different colors but different shades of one basic color, brown.

While many factors are involved in determining skin color and the steps are very technical, basic genetics can help us understand the most important principles.

Assume dominant genes result in lots of melanin and recessive genes result in little melanin. Adam and Eve were most likely a middle brown color with both dominant and recessive genes for the pigment melanin in the skin. Children who received all the dominant genes would end up with a lot of the color and be very dark. Children who received all the recessive genes would end up with only a little color and be very light. Children with a mixture of the genes (both dominant and recessive) would be middle brown.

So, it's not just "black" and "white." Bottom line: a person's skin shade (what is on the outside) should in no way invoke any sort of prejudice or racist comments. What a difference we would see in our world if people reacted in accord with biblical principles, understanding all humans are equal before God, and all are sinners in need of salvation. All of us need to build our thinking on the absolute authority of the Word of God, judging all beliefs and attitudes against the clear teaching of what our Creator God teaches us.

God reminded Samuel of this when He said, "For the LORD does not see as man sees; for man looks at the outward appearance, but the LORD looks at the heart" (1 Samuel 16:7).

(From "Are There Really Different Races?" by Ken Ham in *The New Answers Book 1*)

Video Viewing Guide

Evolutionary Ideas Fueled Racism

> In 1924, the New York Tribune published an article that the missing links were found in Australia, talking about the Australian Aborigines. Did you know that we were taught that the Australian Aborigines were closer to the apes than Caucasians?

> For the World's Fair in 1904, in St. Louis, there was an explorer who brought a pygmy over from South Africa called Ota Benga. They convinced Ota Benga to go into a cage in the Bronx Zoo with an orangutan so that people could come and see the pygmy in the zoo and see the supposed relationship between the pygmy and the orangutan.

> Generations of kids in the public schools in America back in 1925 were being taught from one of the main biology textbooks used in the public schools that the Caucasians were the highest race. No wonder we've got a problem in our nation. No wonder there's a problem even in our churches—the problem of prejudice and racism.

> We need to get rid of the term "races." Instead let's use the term "people groups."

Genetics Shows We're All Related

> As the secular world studies genetics and becomes very much more aware of things from a real observational scientific perspective, they're realizing there's only one race. The major differences are cultural. They're not racial.

> We should be out there as a church saying, "There's only one race. We're all equal before God. We all go back to Adam and Eve. There are different people groups, yes, because of the Tower of Babel, but we all need the same solution —Jesus Christ."

> Within any one people group, the difference genetically between any two people is .2%. But between different groups that were classed as races, the difference that determined that there were different races is .01%. So the difference between any two people within any one group genetically is actually greater than the differences between groups.

> Actually, from a big picture perspective, everybody has the same skin color. There is one basic pigment—melanin—that gives our skin color. Basically, we're all a color that we would call brown. Melanin, it's really a brown pigment. You can be dark brown or light brown, in-between brown.

> If you truly want to see your life reflect the life of Christ, then you must begin to allow Christ to love others through you, particularly those who are different than you, just as He did. You need to begin to see as God sees. When you see the European, the Arab, the Native American, the African American, the Aborigine, the Asian . . . you need to look at them and see your relatives—fellow human beings with the same values and needs you possess. Just like you, they are seeking love, affirmation, and truth. It's time for you to show them the way you have found. Cross the street with your hand outstretched ready to shake the hand of another shade of melanin. Be willing to cross to "the other side of the tracks" to fellowship and worship as a diverse and unified body. (Ken Ham and A. Charles Ware, *One Race, One Blood*, chapter 5).

Interracial Marriage

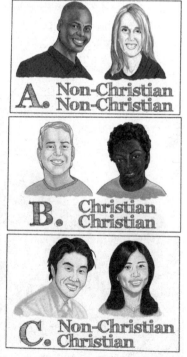

> Biologically there is no such thing—there's only one race.

> Does the Bible say anything about interracial marriage? Yes, it does. It's totally against it. It says the saved race should never knowingly marry the unsaved race.

A. Non-Christian Non-Christian

B. Christian Christian

C. Non-Christian Christian

> Malachi 2:15—because "God seeks godly offspring," you are to produce godly offspring who influence the world for Jesus Christ who produce godly offspring and influence the world for Jesus Christ who produce godly offspring and influence the world for Jesus Christ, generation after generation.

> The family is the first and most fundamental of all human institutions which God ordained in Scripture. And the family is the educational unit that God uses to transmit the knowledge of God from one generation to the next in the world around. And Satan wants to destroy that.

> Parents are often more concerned their son or daughter not marry someone that they think is from a different biological race (when there's no such thing) than whether or not they are of the same spiritual race, which is what marriage is all about.

> But the next time somebody comes into our church and looks a little different externally, how about we look past the small genetic differences and look at the person. Do they need my love? Do they need my help? Do they need the Lord?

> How does God look at people? 1 Samuel 16:7—"For the LORD does not see as a man sees, for the man looks at the outward appearance, but the LORD looks at the heart."

Group Discussion Questions

1. Have you ever been exposed to educational materials that promote the idea of different races? How did they affect you?

2. Why is it important to evangelism to defend that all people groups are descended from Adam?

3. Is evolution the cause of racism? If not, what is?

4. Biologically, how many races are there?

5. Biblically, how many races are there?

6. Is it ever okay for a believer to marry a non-believer? Why or why not?

For Personal Reflection

1. Do you have, or do you know others who have, an "interracial" marriage? What have been some of the challenges?

2. How could you respond to a friend or co-worker who exhibits prejudicial attitudes toward someone else?

For Next Week

Please read and meditate on the following verses in preparation for next week's lesson:

- Genesis 2:15–17, 3:17–19
- Romans 5:12–19
- 1 Corinthians 15:20–26

For Further Study

- Are There Really Different Races? – www.answersingenesis.org/articles/nab/are-there-different-races
- One Race, One Blood – www.answersingenesis.org/articles/orob
- Get Answers: Racism – www.answersingenesis.org/get-answers/topic/racism

Resources

- *One Blood, One Race* by Ken Ham and A. Charles Ware
- *All God's Children* by Ken Ham

Lesson 11: Death the Enemy – Part 1

Objectives

It is our prayer that after you have finished these lessons you will be able to ...

- Answer the question, "Why is there death and suffering in the world?"
- Contrast the biblical view of history with the evolutionary, old-earth view.

Introduction

Why do people suffer? Why do people die? Isn't this a horrible world we live in?

These questions vex not only the unbeliever but the believer as well. Yet as is true in every other question, we should not be ashamed to stand on the authority of God's Word to understand death and suffering.

This question is not as difficult as it might seem. A person only needs to open the Bible and read Genesis chapters 1–3 to find the answer. Here we are told of the beginning of things—God created everything in six ordinary days. We read of a perfect creation in which there was no death. God looked at His creation and called it "very good" (Genesis 1:31).

So where did death come from?

Death came as a direct result of Adam's disobedience. Genesis 2:17 tells us, "But of the tree of the knowledge of good and evil you shall not eat, for in the day that you eat of it you shall surely die." So Adam knew there was a consequence to his actions. When he took of the fruit and ate, death entered God's perfect creation. "For since by man came death, by Man also came the resurrection of the dead" (1 Corinthians 15:21).

Our world is broken, marred by death and suffering. We must understand that our sin is what broke God's perfect creation. The suffering in this world is the first Adam's fault, the consequence of his disobedience to a holy God. We are all sinners because we are descended from sinners and we, too, rebel against God's command (Romans 5:12). Not one is innocent. As a result of sin "the whole creation groans and labors with birth pangs together until now" (Romans 8:22).

The good news is that the Last Adam, Jesus Christ, came to earth to bear the penalty of our sins and be nailed to the Cross. He defeated death by His resurrection. By His atoning blood sacrifice for us, He has made a way for us to spend eternity with Him in heaven. Further, He promised to those who place their faith in Him that in the future there will be no more death, tears, or suffering.

The perfect world will then be restored.

(From "Suffering & Death" by Tommy Mitchell, *Answers*, Jan–Feb, 2010)

Video Viewing Guide

> When we read passages in the Bible about God's love and mercy, and yet we think about tragedy and think about death and suffering in the world, how do we understand a loving God with death and suffering?

> Many Christians, as a witness to non-Christians, say, "Can't you see this beautiful world that God made?" But you know, when we look at it, it's not so beautiful, is it? Yeah, there's beauty out there, but there's a lot of ugliness, too.

> At the same time we see beauty, we also see a world where we see sorrow; we see joy, we see sorrow; we see life, we see death; we see love, we see hate— all at the same time. So how do we put all that together? How do we understand that?

> Right there in Genesis, God made two trees, the tree of the knowledge of good and evil and the tree of life. And actually, the tree of the knowledge of good and evil can be called the tree of death, because, "Adam, if you eat of this tree, you will surely die."

> God sustains everything by the power of His Word. Jesus Christ holds all things together. By Him, all things consist. And when God created and said everything was "very good," He held everything together perfectly. It was very good. There was no death, no suffering, no tragedy.

> And when Adam sinned God withdrew some of that sustaining power because the Bible now says it's a groaning world, it's running down because of sin. God withdrew some of that sustaining power so everything would run down, so we would run down, so we would die.

As children of Adam, we all inherit Adam's sin nature. We have all, at some point, disobeyed a command from the Creator, so we all deserve to die and suffer eternal punishment in hell. We must understand that not one of us is innocent before God. Romans 3:23 says, "For all have sinned and fall short of the glory of God." Not one of us is worthy to stand before the Creator of the universe because we would each bring a sinful, rebellious nature into His presence. (Tommy Mitchell, "Why Does God's Creation Include Death & Suffering," *The New Answers Book 1*)

› We forfeited our right to live because we, in Adam, sinned. Adam was the head of the human race. What he did, we did. We sinned in him. We came from him. He represented us. And our bodies will die.

› God killed at least one animal and clothed Adam and Eve. But we are made in the image of God. We're not like the animals. And an animal can't take away our sin. The blood of bulls and goats can't take away our sin.

› The Israelites sacrificed animals over and over and over again because it was a picture of what was to come in Jesus Christ, who's called the Last Adam. The Son of God stepped into history to be Jesus the God-man to die on a Cross because death was the penalty for sin.

› It doesn't matter who we are and what situation we're in; none of us deserve anything. We don't deserve a thing; doesn't matter who we are. God stepped into history to save us and offer us a free gift of salvation so we can spend eternity with Him.

› What are we taught today from the secular perspective?

> We're taught this from the secular perspective: "The secrets of evolution are time and death; time for the slow accumulation of favorable mutations, and death, to make room for new species."

> Evolution puts time and death together—time and death; millions of years of death, suffering, disease, bloodshed—death over millions of years leading up to man. Is it any wonder that students who are taught that that's their history in school commit acts of school violence?

Group Discussion Questions

1. If someone came to your church and asked the question "If God is love, why is there suffering and death?" what might the average member say? How would your pastor respond?

2. Do you agree that it is not accurate to use "the beauty in nature" as an example of God's love and creativity? Why or why not? How do you think nature should be used for evangelism?

3. Do you know of other people who, like Ted Turner and Charles Darwin, abandoned their faith in God after the devastating death of a loved one? What other tragic circumstances might cause someone to question God?

4. Describe in your own words the secular humanist belief in "time and death."

5.   Describe in your own words the biblical view of "sin and death."

For Personal Reflection

1.   If someone asked you why bad things happen to good people, what would you say?

2.   In what ways has the Christian life not lived up to your expectations? What specific circumstances cause you to doubt God's goodness or power?

3.   Do you have a good answer to "the question"? If you don't, how might that affect your faith in the future? How might your life be different if you had a clear and concise answer to this important question?

4.   Spend some time alone with the Lord, asking Him to search your heart and reveal your ways (Psalm 139:23). In what ways do you need to "bend the knee" before Him as your sovereign Lord?

For Next Week

Please read and meditate on the following verses in preparation for next week's lesson:

- Job 42:1–6
- Romans 8:28–30
- John 3:1–8; Revelation 20:11–15

For Further Study

- Two Histories of Death – www.answersingenesis.org/creation/v24/i1/history.asp
- Why Does God's Creation Include Death and Suffering? – www.answersingenesis.org/articles/nab/why-does-creation-include-suffering

Resources

- *How Could a Loving God?* by Ken Ham & Stephen Ham, Master Books
- *A God of Suffering?* (DVD) featuring Tommy Mitchell, Answers in Genesis

Lesson 12: Death the Enemy – Part 2

Objectives

It is our prayer that after you have finished these lessons you will be able to . . .

- Identify that without the Bible as a foundation, man has no basis for making moral judgments.
- Realize that tragedies and disasters should lead people to repentance.
- Humbly bow before God as the one in control of all things.

Introduction

I often quote the Book of Job in my talks on Genesis. But you know one of the most important things we learn from the Book of Job? We find God asks Job a series of questions: Do you know this, Job? What about this? God uses example after example to finally bring Job to the point in Job 42 where we read:

> Then Job answered the LORD and said: "I know that You can do everything, and that no purpose of Yours can be withheld from You. . . . Therefore I have uttered what I did not understand, things too wonderful for me, which I did not know. . . . Therefore I abhor myself, and repent in dust and ashes." (Job 42:1–6)

Basically, this is the answer to the issue of death and suffering. Job acknowledged that compared to what God knows, he knew nothing. He repented of his human arrogance and totally submitted his life to the all-knowing sovereign God.

The bottom line is that we are not going to have all the answers as to why things like Rob's sickness have been allowed to happen. Only God knows everything—we are just fallible human beings who, like Job, need to recognize that we know nothing compared to what God knows.

The Bible's account of origins in Genesis, however, does make sense of the world around us. This has greatly helped me in dealing with the issue of death and suffering. God's Word tells us clearly where death and sickness originated. We understand we live in a fallen world. Every person needs to be spiritually healed, and total healing doesn't come until we leave this sin-cursed universe.

God has a sovereign plan far greater than we could imagine. Thus, we need to put our trust in God's Word and the fact that He is in total control. "It is the LORD. Let Him do what seems good to Him" (1 Samuel 3:18).

Yes, sickness, suffering and death are a normal part of this life. But: "Blessed be the God and Father of our Lord Jesus Christ, the Father of mercies and God of all comfort" (2 Corinthians 1:3).

(From "Walking Through Shadows" by Ken Ham, www.answersingenesis. org/articles/2002/07/29/walking-through-shadows)

Video Viewing Guide

> Evolution is really a tree of death because what we're taught by the secularists is that death over millions of years is a part of the evolutionary process bringing different kinds of animals and plants into existence and eventually man.

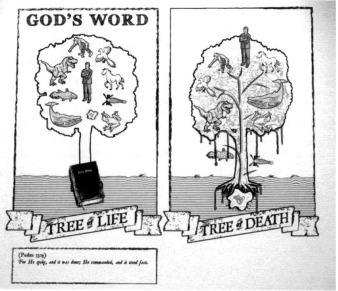

> The Bible tells us God created distinct kinds of animals and plants to start with and that everything was "very good." There wasn't any death in the world. It started as a tree of life.

> Evolution and millions of years puts time and death together. The Bible doesn't do that. The Bible puts sin and death together. Death is a consequence of sin. Death is, as it says in 1 Corinthians 15:26, an enemy.

> Unless you have an absolute authority, how do you determine what's right and what's wrong? How do you determine what's just and what's unjust? How can a non-Christian accuse God of being unjust?

> Ultimately, from an ultimate perspective, only Christians have a basis to make moral judgments. Non-Christians ultimately actually have no basis to make moral judgments.

> Philosophically speaking, the problem of evil actually is a problem for the unbeliever. They think it's a problem for the believer. It's not, it's a problem for the unbeliever, because how can they determine that something's evil or something's wrong or someone's unjust? They can't do that.

> We look at it from a human perspective, and here we are judging God, saying, "Well, I don't understand. It doesn't make sense. Why would You let this happen and why would You let that happen and why would all this happen?" Is it possible that there are morally commendable, just reasons for it and we just don't know what they are? Is that possible?

> Job recognized this: "Compared to God, I know nothing. God is infinite in knowledge, infinite in wisdom. As a finite being, compared to what God knows, I know nothing."

> How dare we as fallible human beings listen to the fallible teachings of secular man and we take that and we reinterpret God's Word. How dare we? Job recognized that he needed to let God be God; that we don't know what God knows.

When the dark times come, God offers no apologies and gives few explanations—and He takes responsibility for all that is taking place. I the Lord do all these things. Pour out your heart, if you wish, but don't argue. I'm God, you are not. Period. You have no clue about what I am doing and what will come of it.

Yes, God is the one who raises up kingdoms and destroys them. He's in charge of those sorts of things. He is a sovereign God and so nothing happens that He doesn't know about. As one of my friends said, "God has yet to make His first mistake, because God is in total control." That's not a cop-out; that's simply allowing God to be God. Make no mistake on this point. God is very firm. He is who He is, and He has absolutely no obligation to us to change anything according to our desires, nor should He be compelled to alter His plans to pander to our feelings. (Stephen Ham, *How Could a Loving God?*, epilogue)

> You know whose fault it is that those children died in Indonesia from that tsunami? It's our fault because we sinned. It's my fault. We sinned against a Holy God. It's not God's fault. It's our fault. But you know, the right question is not why did those children die? You know what the right question is? Why is everyone going to die?

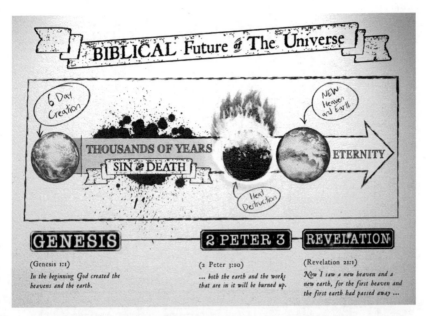

BIBLICAL Future of The Universe

6 Day Creation

NEW Heaven and Earth

THOUSANDS OF YEARS
SIN & DEATH

Heat Destruction

ETERNITY

GENESIS — **2 PETER 3** — **REVELATION**

(Genesis 1:1)
In the beginning God created the heavens and the earth.

(2 Peter 3:10)
... both the earth and the works that are in it will be burned up.

(Revelation 21:1)
Now I saw a new heaven and a new earth, for the first heaven and the first earth had passed away ...

> Do you know what the Bible says? There was a beginning. God created it. He created time, created a space-mass-time universe. He created human beings. But you know, there's not going to be an end in which that's the end of it all. There's going to be a judgment and there's going to be a new heavens and a new earth. And those that have trusted Christ will live with Him forever. Those that don't will be separated from Him forever.

> The Bible warns us of something, that if you're only born once you're going to die twice. You die physically and then you die again because you're separated from God for eternity. But if you're born twice, you only die once.

Group Discussion Questions

1. If, indeed, God uses the suffering and death of some individuals to bring blessings to others, do you think He is being fair? Why or why not?

2. What situations in your life can you think of where God caused something to work for good, even though it was evil? Was His goodness apparent at the time of the event?

3. When people face suffering and death, how might their emotional response (depression, anger, joy, peace, etc.) reveal their level of belief in the truths of Romans 8:28?

For Personal Reflection

1. Many times, the good that God is working out through difficult circumstances results in inner changes of character and faith that make us more like Christ. In what ways has the suffering and death you've experienced resulted in inner change? In most situations, do you tend to reject or embrace these changes?

2. What current situations are you facing that seem to be evil or wrong? Are you able to see God's goodness at work, or do you think it will take the perspective of time to see the result of His purpose?

3. Are you willing to accept by faith the suffering and death as something that God can work out and is working out for good? If so, spend some time praying, thanking Him for every circumstance that surrounds you.

For Further Study

- Two Histories of Death – www.answersingenesis.org/creation/v24/i1/history.asp
- Why Does God's Creation Include Death and Suffering? – www.answersingenesis.org/articles/nab/why-does-creation-include-suffering

Resources

- *How Could a Loving God?* by Ken Ham & Stephen Ham, Master Books
- *A God of Suffering?* (DVD) featuring Tommy Mitchell, Answers in Genesis